KU-335-644

Joseph Corvo

The Miracle
of You

Corvoline

This book is available from Corvoline
7 Belsize Square, London NW3 4HT Price £2.45
plus 30p postage.

The L.P. recording "REGAIN THE JOY OF
LIVING" can also be obtained. Price £3.50, including
postage.

© 1981, Joseph Corvo

Cover design by Jean Bird

ISBN 0 9507433 0 5

Printed by Villiers Publications Ltd.,
Ingestre Road, London NW5

PREFACE

Always remember that Zone Therapy is only a God-sent aid to your wellbeing. The main healer is the God within you for without God you are nowhere.

Zone treatment is God's treatment. I cannot emphasise that fact hard enough so unless God is there in your thoughts success will be most difficult.

God never passes by unnoticed any prayer. He walks within the silence and his benedictions rest on every effort of the soul. So when you pray, go to the deepest room of your soul. Close the door and in the holy silence, pray. For what you write on the inside you will experience on the outside. If you cultivate the bliss and quietness of inner joyousness you can climb to any heights and you can be the best at whatever you choose to do. There will be that lovely light in your eye which is the light of the inspired. You have passed from the mundane into spiritual enlightenment.

The really successful man is not the one who has accumulated a lot of money, properties and worldly possessions. The truly successful man is the one who gives to the world creative expressions of magnitude to the benefit of mankind by courtesy of the Infinite Intelligence and Cosmic Order.

The Universe holds all the secrets. Mankind must eventually learn through the subconscious mind how to make contact with all knowledge; it requires Faith, Confidence and Love.

JOSEPH CORVO

The author, Joseph Corvo, explains to us in this his first book how we can acquire perfect health in the physical body. He also informs us that the Thinking Body, the Feeling Body and the Acting Body must also be activated to maximum health because this opens up the doorway to the subconscious mind which is the Golden Gateway to Infinite Intelligence and Universal Law.

Jesus said: 'For this is He, of whom it is written;'
'Behold I send a messenger to prepare a way.'
St. Matthew, Ch. 11, verses 10 and 15

CONTENTS

INTRODUCTION

Over the many years that I have been a practising healer using Zone Therapy I have constantly been urged by people all over the world to write a book about this wonderful work. I have at last accomplished that task.

In the time that I have applied this form of treatment to patients the most wonderful results have followed, some of them miraculous.

This method is absolutely natural and safe. It decongests and eliminates poisons from the body and allows the glands and nervous systems to work without impediment or obstruction.

With excellent health it is possible to gain riches and prosperity, peace of mind, love and happiness. You will find new inner strength. For a body that is glowing with superb health releases the spiritual power within you. When a man or woman suffers from sickness everything about them is focused upon that illness and they are then unable to progress. The key to everything you desire depends firstly upon superb physical health which will automatically bring about good mental health. These two factors allow the spiritual part of you to work unimpeded.

If any gland in your body is malfunctioning you can never be at your best. Your mental body depends upon your physical body. Therefore any glandular disturbance will make you unhappy. When you see a man very happy and prosperous he is usually very healthy and when you see a man poor and unhappy he, alas, is usually not so healthy. There are many good kind religious people who suffer the tortures of the damned in mind and body. What a boon superb health would be to those people.

It is possible to recapture the days of your youth, to feel the miraculous self-renewing power flowing through you. Once again the feeling of inspiration can lift, rejuvenate, revitalize, recharge your mind and spirit. You can bubble over with enthusiasm and joy as in the days of your youth. Because with a healthy body all this is your heritage.

Within each one of us there is that part which houses the Infinite Intelligence, the secret store of all knowledge. And how do we unlock the door to this Intelligence? It can be done if all parts of a person are in perfect balance. You must start with the physical body and then work inwards to the mental body and spiritual body. This is what makes you a whole person. And when you are a whole person then patience, kindness, love, goodwill, joy, happiness, wisdom and understanding are part of you. God is life. You are part of that life. Life is self renewing, eternal and indestructible and because your life is God's life, you live for ever. Remember there are so many parts of you that you cannot see. Your mind — but you know you have a mind. You cannot see your spirit but you know you have a spirit. You cannot see the Infinite Intelligence within you but it is there. All these things are part of you.

All things are possible. Formulate ideas and visualize them as if they are living things. Your physical eyes can only see physical things, external matter, but your mind's eye can visualize the future of things to come. The pictures in your mind are substance of things which you hope for and, of course, absolute evidence of things not seen. The things you imagine are real and will happen if you have the faith to believe in them. Your mental images can become absolute reality. If you constantly hold beautiful thoughts you will become beautiful. If you hold ugly thoughts you will become ugly. This is the law of cause and effect. If you spend your life thinking negatively and destructively, spreading unhappiness like the plague, you will undoubtedly finish up very sick, mostly heart troubles, malignancies and, of course, chronic nervous disorder. You are what you think you are. Millions of people today spend one-third of their lives sleeping, and two-thirds not feeling well. I want to help you to change all that.

We in our so-called civilized society are inundated with a lot of talk and very little action. Simply sitting down and praying is not the answer to the problem. Prayer is the most wonderful thing but it must be allied to positive action. This is fulfilling God's Law — prayer and action. In this book I am giving guidance towards selp helf in a very simple way and hope as a result that a better life pattern will evolve for you. God bless you.

WHAT IS ZONE THERAPY?

It is based on the theory of ten main zones running through the body, ten invisible electrical zones. These electrical forces end in the feet, hands, face, head and back. Crystallized deposits form around these nerve endings and this causes havoc with circulation to the body, the power of electro magnetics through the system is greatly reduced and the eventual result over a period of time is sickness.

RELAXING

There can be few better ways to make a person feel completely relaxed. It is a Godly form of treatment because it is so natural and through natural means restores the body to normal function. The nervous systems respond magnificently and nervous people become very relaxed.

WHAT DOES IT DO?

When the Creator put you together and you are the most complex machine ever invented, He built into you a mechanism that will correct any malfunctioning. Over many years doing my healing work through this treatment, I have discovered some of that mechanism and can therefore only report upon my own findings which have often been miraculous. It purifies the physical bodily systems by eliminating toxins and poisons.

THE HEALING EFFECTS

Zoneology can produce the most wonderful results. Pain can be relieved, organs can move from abnormal to normal positions, eyesight can be corrected, deaf ears can often be made to hear, weak livers and kidneys, faulty adrenals all respond to this treatment. When this form of healing is finally understood it will offer unlimited scope and open up fields never before thought of. A new way will finally emerge.

THE POWER OF PRAYER

Remember that your subconscious mind holds the absolute power. It is the source of infinite wisdom and all great healings must take place through the subconscious mind. Relax quietly. Let your thoughts go God-wise. Imagine yourself in perfect health. Believe in perfect health, see yourself as being physically perfect. The secret of success flows through the power of Infinite Intelligence. Faith will move mountains.

Chapter 1

THE MIRACLE OF YOU

Congratulations! You have entered the wonderful world of getting your body into perfect shape. From this day on you are going to progress until your body becomes a wonderful thing to behold. Because by reading this book you are one of the special people who have taken steps to improve yourself physically and mentally. You will never look back. From now on the world can become a different place for you. The fact that you have been interested enough to purchase this book and to be serious enough to read it and to be inspired by what you read, will automatically help you to improve your physical condition and overall appearance. If you work well you will wind up eventually with the utmost strength, health and fitness.

Your glands and your nervous systems are what make you function. Make no mistake about it. And if you do your best to see that your glands and nervous systems are working perfectly then, before your very eyes, you are going to transform yourself into the kind of person you have always wanted to be, and you can go all the way towards physical perfection with flying colours.

THE SECRET OF SUCCESS

The secret of success is desire. Every man has genius within him although some appear to have it more than others, only because they are aware of it more than others are and because the awareness or the unawareness of desire is what makes each one of them into a success or a mediocrity.

A lot of mediocrity that we see around us is self-inflicted and most of the genius that we see around is brought about by the desire to succeed. If we lack desire we are mediocre. If we have an abundance of desire we will become mostly successful. This applies to everything you do. If you are going to work towards gaining a beautiful body then the desire to do so has to be there. It is the key to success.

CIRCULATION

Circulation is of vital importance in order to have a body that is free from congestion and the thousand and one ailments which are caused by this condition. For you cannot deny that circulation is life. The opposite of that is stagnation and the opposite to life is death. So any part of your body that has been cut off from its proper normal circulation is going to start to deteriorate in a very short time. That deterioration will begin to affect other parts of your body until eventually all parts of your body become congested. At this point decay is beginning to set in rapidly.

Unfortunately the majority of people wait until only a miracle is going to help them. That is why this system, this zonal system, is so important to you, as a preventive method it has no peers.

BALANCE

Remember a healthy body makes a like mind, an equation, a balance. Everything in the universe is the result of balance. Where there is imbalance or unbalance there is chaos. You can see the state that mankind is in to know the devastation that imbalance and unbalance can bring about. Study a tree, how sturdy is the oak, harmless, beautiful, quiet and peaceful, throwing wide and open its arms heavenwards, praising God as it were. If we can emulate the peace, quietness, stability and the strength of trees we would be living in a far better world than we are.

You can therefore see the wonders that lie before us if we are prepared to keep our bodies in beautiful condition, every part working in rhythm and harmony. Always remember that nature will help you if you give nature the chance to help you.

YOUR EYES

Think what a living miracle you are. What a most miraculous thing the human being is. Think of your eyes which enable you to see, then imagine being blind. How fortunate you are to be able to see the sun rise and set, to be able to see a cloud or a flower, a child or a rainbow; to be able to see the beautiful things which are in the world and to be able to see the look of love from someone who loves you. Isn't this the most miraculous thing, and you possess it. Think of all the many thousands of fibres there must be in your ears which vibrate to help you to hear music, birds singing, children laughing. Isn't that beautiful? The fact that you can speak, you can communicate, and think of the poor friends around us in the animal kingdom who are restricted from conversing with the fluency that you are able to converse with.

EXPRESSION

How fortunate you are to be able to speak and talk and express yourself to others. Isn't that miraculous?

You can stand up straight and move about, whilst a flower or a plant or a tree has to remain rooted in one spot. You are able to travel about, to move from one part of the planet to another if you so desire.

You can see, you can hear and you have mobility. This is the most wonderful thing.

Do you know that within your body you have 500 muscles and 200 bones and you have miles of nerves which are synchronised to do what you wish. How wonderful. You have the ability to love someone and for someone to love you. Think of the joy such a thing can bring. Think how marvellous it is to enjoy and to receive the gift of love.

THE HEART

Think of your heart. There it is in beautiful rhythm working away minute after minute, day after day, month after month and year after year, whether you are asleep or awake. Your blood moves through thousands of miles of veins and arteries pumping hundreds of thousands of gallons a year through you. Isn't this the most wonderful thing.

LUNGS

Think of the way your lungs function as the breath of life enters your body. Your lungs are the portholes because they give you life support and even in the most terrible conditions that exist with pollution today, your lungs work away to filter life-giving oxygen to you. They get rid of all the excess waste in the process. Think what a wonderful function they perform.

CELLS

Think of all the millions of blood cells. Within each cell are millions of molecules reproducing. Your cells reproduce themselves continually. All of this is going on inside you and you take it for granted. Yet you are the most beautiful complex creation.

The weight of your brain is 3 lbs. and yet within it there are billions of nerve cells. They file away every sound, every impression, taste and smell, every action that you ever experience is recorded there and waiting to be brought back at a moment's notice. And you have all the wonderful touch detectors, and you possess the mechanism that keeps your temperature down to the right level. All this goes on inside the human body.

HEALTH

If you have health you have everything. Money, wealth, material possessions, mean nothing if you are sick, chronically sick. The greatest treasure, the greatest wealth ever known is superb health. With superb health the world is a great place. So when you are feeling depressed, downhearted or irritated, cursing your luck, take a good look at yourself and if you are in superb health, then take yourself to task and say, look, I have the greatest treasure in all of this world, my health.

Poverty can be overcome, success and happiness can be sought, but if you are rich with material wealth and you are old and you are sick and you are helpless and weak, you don't have very much.

I would rather be a beggar with superb health than be the wealthiest man in this world with chronic ill health.

When you go to bed at night and you know that every part of your body is working perfectly, then say your prayers and be grateful — count your blessings — and make a point of never moaning again.

MIRACLE OF MIRACLES

The human being is certainly the miracle of miracles. Out of all the billions of people that walk this planet, do you know that there are not two people exactly alike. Each one is different. Each one is absolutely unique. You can thank the creator for that. This is God's blessing. You possess the ability to think, to imagine, to create, to speak, to pray, to plan and to love. Decide now not to hate or destroy or wound or procrastinate. Everything is possible for you because you are absolutely unique, a special creation.

Think of the power that lies within the physical body, all the glands, nervous systems and organs, the way it works and the way it performs at your will. No greater treasure in this world do you possess than your body.

CAPABILITY

Be more concerned with your body and less concerned with material things. This is the only body you have and you cannot exchange it like you can a car. There is nothing you cannot do, you are capable of the greatest wonders. The potential within you is unlimited. Most things have been mastered by man, including gravity and space and many diseases have been overcome, and pestilence. All this man has achieved.

Never underestimate yourself. Don't put yourself down and always go for the best things in life in a fair and reasonable way. If you have talent, and most of us have, don't hide it. Don't lack confidence. Everything is there in front of you. Give of your best in whatever you do. No matter how big or small the task may be, give more than you expect in return.

CHOICE

Think of the wonderful things you are able to choose to do. Choice — what a wonderful thing it is to be able to choose. The human being possesses that capability.

All this is possible if you will start to think about your body. You belong to that special band of people who are concerned with getting themselves better and fitter. The fitter you are, the better you are going to feel, the more kindly disposed you are going to be. Think of your glands working perfectly, your nervous systems working perfectly. This usually means that you will be fair-minded because there is peace within you when you acquire this. Worry and anxiety can become a thing of the past for, with a fit, superb body and mind, nothing is able to worry you.

Success or failure is yours for the choosing. Take a good look at yourself. Decide from this day on that mediocrity as far as you are concerned is going to be a thing of the past.

HOW TO ACQUIRE SUCCESS

The first thing must be to see that your body is in absolutely superb shape and fitness. This is a must. Start to think of the glands, the different places they are in. Close your eyes and try to imagine that you can see your glands working for you and in this way you can soon build up a mental conversation with all your glandular systems. You are able to start to go inside and see them actually working inside you in the mind's eye. This helps you to become on the most intimate terms with your own body, knowing exactly how it works and how it functions.

CONVERSE WITHIN

If you start to converse within yourself with your glandular systems, those glands in turn will appreciate the fact that you are showing concern and interest about their welfare. It sounds silly doesn't it? I ask you to give it a try. I ask you to put it into practice. If all of us could be more concerned with how our own bodies work, we would be more caring about our fellow men because we would begin to realise what a wonderful and unique personality each one is. We would appreciate more the wonderful gifts human beings possess, this beautiful machine we call a physical body. In this way it would open up new fields of thought, of action. We would most certainly care for each other a lot more than we ever thought possible.

NO ACCIDENT

You will begin to see that you are no accident. You will begin to see that the greatest scientist, the greatest inventor of all, put you together and made you what you are. So no more pity. Stand up straight and be determined to change your life and to make your life worth living. What a challenge for you and what a wonderful success story at the end of the day when you have achieved superb and perfect health. For there is no doubt about it, each and every human being is indeed a living miracle.

Chapter 2

THE GLANDS

The Adrenals

The adrenal glands are situated just above the kidneys, they are known as the glands of fight and flight. When you experience any emotion such as anger or fear a large amount of the hormone from the adrenal glands know as Adrenalin pours into the blood and prepares the body for action. The adrenalin causes the body starch or glycogen stored in the liver and muscles to be broken down to sugar, ready to serve as a source of energy for immediate action.

Any deficiency of adrenalin therefore will cause slowness of reaction and the inability to cope when danger threatens.

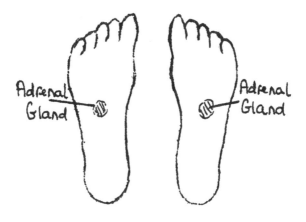

The Thyroid Gland

The glands on either side of the throat are known as the thyroid glands. They produce a hormone which is called Thyroxine. It contains iodine. The thyroid glands become abnormal when iodine is constantly deficient in the diet for an appreciable period of time. Therefore if the iodine intake is low, the gland enlarges to compensate for the lack of iodine. The resulting enlargement is known as a goitre. Goitres will disappear when the correct amount of iodine is supplied, together with an entirely health building programme.

Iodine is essential for normal working of the thyroid gland. Thyroxine is poured into the blood and it is carried to all parts of the body. It tells the cells in the body to burn the amount of food necessary to produce the amount of energy needed to maintain a normal body temperature. Thyroxine does a great deal to keep the heart beating at the rate which will create normal circulation to all parts of the body. If sufficient iodine is not supplied this will result in the amount of Thyroxine not being produced. When this happens the body activities do become sluggish, the breathing is heavier and more deliberate than normal, the heart tends to beat slowly and there are contractions in the digestive tract which leads to indigestion and constipation. With this lack of energy we find that changes start and abnormalities creep in. If you lack iodine you become tired, no endurance, you put on weight and develop poor circulation, have cold hands and feet, your skin becomes scaley, lifeless hair, lack-lustre and often falling out, finger nails split or break, your memory starts to suffer because of poor circulation to the brain.

In females menstruation is put into an unbalanced state, you develop headaches and there is a general slowing down. You can therefore see how vitally important it is to make certain that your thyroid gland does work efficiently.

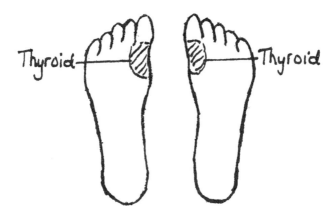

The Lymphatic System

The lymph glands produce a fluid which is almost colourless, very slightly tinged with yellow. It has a salty taste and it reaches all parts of the body which are not reached by the blood. It supplies the cells with what they need to carry on their functions. A continual change between the lymph and the blood is going on all the time. We have what are known as lymph nodes. These are small bodies which are in the line of flow of the lymphatic fluid. Basically there are two sets of nodes, the superficial and the deep set. They are located on the back of the head and they drain back to the tongue, the nose, the pharynx and the mouth. The lymphatic system must be kept in absolutely perfect condition if you want to enjoy good health because the nodes act as filters. Their job is to prevent infection.

The endocrine glands

The endocrine glands consist of the penial gland, pituitary gland, parathyroids, thyroid, thymus, suprenals, pancreas, the ovaries or testes. The endocrine system affects the emotions of the mind. These glands are also known as ductless glands because they pass their secretions directly into the blood or lymph instead of into excretiary ducts. Full growth and function of the various parts of the body are possible only when there is a balanced activity of the internal secretion glands. These secretions are called hormones which means to excite or arouse and their effect can be immediate or delayed. They are simple chemical substances which must be oxidised and excreted after they have exerted their specific benefits.

If these secretions suffer, pathological conditions in different parts of the body are rapidly established. Mental emotions such as fear, sorrow, anger, jealousy, hatred, love and envy have been noted to affect our bodies especially the endocrine system and nervous systems, according to the degree of intensity. These emotions are like shock waves affecting the nervous system and leading to the degeneration of the endocrine glands. The endocrine system is controlled by the sympathetic and vagus nerves. When the emotions are not very severe they may not cause actual physical death but definitely they do affect the nervous and endocrine systems.

An effect of emotional reaction is of course high blood pressure. Where there is fear or anger it is common to notice a faster heartbeat. Emotions affect the adrenal gland. It secretes extra doses of adrenalin, the adrenalin increases in the blood stream, accelerates the heart beat and raises the blood pressure.

These mental emotions strain the heart causing nervous disorders and heart complaints.

The Kidneys

They may be loosened or floating or enlarged or they can be below the normal size. They may secrete too much or not enough urine. Any abnormality with the kidneys will interfere with the general health of each person. It is important to see that the kidneys are free from all crystalline deposits.

As circulation is responsible for all bodily functions, the kidneys eliminate poisons from the system so we must do anything we can to increase the circulation to enable the kidneys to greater efficiency in carrying off the toxins and poisons of the system.

We have two kidneys one on the right side of the body and one on the left. Thus we find it is quite easy by looking at the chart to find the nerve corresponding to either the right kidney or the left kidney. Always be gentle when you are massaging the kidney reflex. It has to be treated with a bit more care than other glands for the reaction can be a little bit devastating to the patient. So take it easy when you are working over the kidney reflex. Do it with a nice gentle pressure, not too deep, not too hard and not too strong. Be patient and work this particular gland say twice a week. Remember that the kidney is most important in the elimination of uric acids from the system and often in cases of eczema you will find that by work over the kidney you will be able to help the pores of the skin to eliminate the poison.

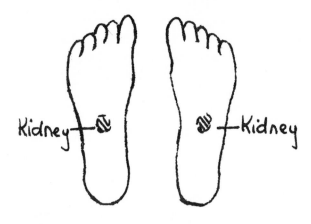

Kidney   Kidney

The Liver

The liver is the biggest gland in the body. It is in the right side of the body and weighs about 3 lbs. Its transverse diameter is about 11 inches and its greatest vertical is about 5 to 7 inches. It is known as the king of the glands because it is the biggest organ in the body and at all times about one quarter of the blood of the body is circulating through it. It performs quite a few tasks. It makes bile to digest fats, it is antiseptic and it helps to supply substances for making blood. It also stores up sugar within itself, it filters and lubricates and prevents constipation.

It has to function properly and correctly to enable it to perform its task of circulation.

Therefore we must see that the circulation is regularly stimulated. If you should therefore find tenderness around the region of the liver as shown on your chart, you will know that the liver is sluggish and therefore it cannot be functioning properly. We know that if this goes on it will impede circulation and over the months and years we know that it will weaken the functions of the liver which then could result in many diseases such as jaundice, diabetes, gallstones, sclerosis, constitpation. We must make certain that this major gland functions properly.

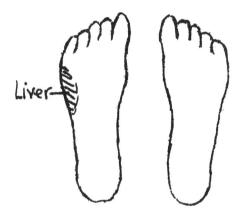

Liver

Ovaries

To keep the Ovaries in a perfectly healthy condition means to keep them free from congestion. The central nervous system must be working properly which means having a peaceful and happy life style. Also most essential to the health of the ovaries must be a normal regular sex life, that is, regular climax must be the rule as frustration can cause frigidity and eventually fibroid tumours. Dissatisfaction in the sex life of two people can cause havoc with the ovaries in women and prostate trouble in men.

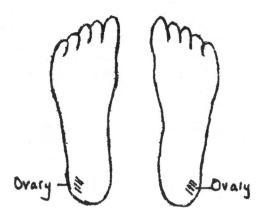

Ovary — Ovaly

The Pancreas

The Pancreas is a gland which is situated below the stomach. It secretes a most important hormone know as insulin. Now the purpose of insulin is to help the body to store sugar in the form of starch or glycogen and also in burning sugar to produce energy. As foods digest, sugar pours out from the intestinal tract into the blood. The pancreas then secretes insulin which is carried by the blood. The liver and muscles throughout the body are then told to withdraw the sugar not needed for energy production from the blood and store it as starch or glycogen. If we do any damage to the pancreas so that insulin can no longer be produced, the amount of sugar from digesting foods collects in the blood and is lost in the urine so the sugar cannot be used for energy. To produce enough energy through the burning of fat a definite proportion of sugar or glycogen which is muscle sugar must be burned along with the fat. Abnormalities can occur when the pancreas no longer can produce sufficient insulin. This condition is then known as Diabetes.

So then again I say, how important it is to see that you keep the pancreas in top condition.

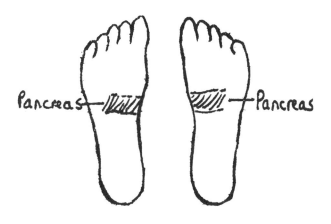

The Pituitary Gland

This is the master gland. It is situated at the base of the brain and just above the back of the throat. It is protected with great strength. It secretes hormones that activate and control important glands of the body. The pituitary also secretes gonad hormones which stimulate and activate the sex glands of both sexes. It also stimulates the thyroid gland and controls the growth of the body. And when it is over produced this accounts for giants, people who grow to be seven feet tall are the result of over production of the pituitary gland. It is a most vital gland to keep in perfect condition because it is the master gland. If anything goes wrong with the pituitary gland the rest of the body is bound to suffer.

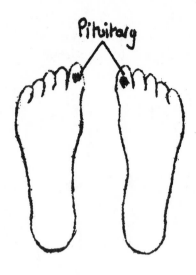

The Prostate Gland

This causes problems amongst men usually after the age of about 45. The prostate gland is situated around the neck of the urinary bladder and its purpose is to supply fluid to carry sperm. If it becomes inflamed and swollen the urethra or canal leading from the bladder to the outside of the body is pinched together and it makes it difficult for the bladder to empty. When the bladder is filled the pressure from above can become great enough to force open the urethra but often when half empty the force of the swollen gland is greater than that of the liquid and the urethra closes again. At any time when urination becomes difficult, inflammation of the prostate gland must be a possibility, and you should therefore make absolutely certain that your prostate gland is working perfectly.

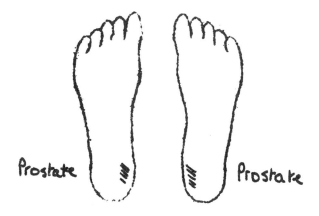

Prostate Prostate

Chapter 3

ZONE THERAPY

Zone Therapy can be used for all kinds of complaints. Pressure can be exerted over any painful reflex on the feet and hands and arms and legs. Remember that the system is as old as the human race. Remember, too, that this system was born into you — you were born with it.

If you bang your head against a door, the first thing you instinctively do is to put your hand over the painful part and press it, because you instinctively feel the comfort coming from such an action. If you hit your thumb with a hammer, apart from cursing, the next thing you do is to grab hold of the thumb and hold it very tightly. You are applying pressure again to give comfort. If any part of your body is in pain, you usually put your hand over it instinctively. This just proves to you that to pressurise parts of your body is born within you. Your subconscious possesses the knowledge that pressure eases the shock.

All through the ages there have been men who were in possession of the knowledge of this treatment, who were looked upon as supermen because they were able to do what ordinary people could not do. They were able to touch a person, give a little bit of pressure, the pain would disappear and the man would be looked upon as a miracle worker and held in awe.

As I have said before, it is a God-sent treatment and it has one advantage over any other method because not only does it relieve the effect but it removes the cause. Remember that you cannot injure yourself in any way using the zonery system. It is completely harmless and absolutely safe.

If you are working on your fingers for your eyes or ears, gradually work over the top joint until you find the most sensitive spot. That is the reflex that needs work on it. It is better to do short treatments several times in the week. The zones of the body vary in position slightly in each individual person so the areas I give you are approximately the areas. If you don't find it exactly as on your chart, either go slightly below, slightly above, or to the side and you will contact the right point.

Don't forget that when you are working on any reflex or zone area in the body, not only are you rectifying that particular gland but any other trouble in that particular zone will also be purified and brought back to normal working. So it is best to try if you can to prevent corns, bunions, etc., growing on the foot, because these often sit over the top of a reflex and then it is impossible to work that reflex. You can see the sense in trying to prevent these things growing on your feet. Corns and bunions are brought about by shoes which don't fit properly.

The greatest advantage of using Zone Therapy is that you can treat yourself at home, but you have to be persistent. You have to be determined. Use a bit of faith and a little bit of intelligence. By doing this, you can say that you have taken out an insurance which will help to keep you in good condition.

Think about your body. How are your bowels working? Are you constipated? Think of your diet. What do you eat and drink? Think about the way you breathe. Are you breathing correctly? Rectify all this. Look at your tongue, your teeth, your eyes. You have to keep a constant surveillance over your body to bring about a fit condition. Notice those things that are not working correctly and start to rectify them. Don't forget that your body is a very lazy thing, and yet you can make it do anything. If you obey all the laws of natural health, you can make your body strong and it will resist all disease. Disease manifests in the body because of the lack of resistance.

If Zone Treatment were practised regularly millions could enjoy full rich lives instead of misery and despair. For, if the nervous systems, the glandular systems and the organs of the body are kept in perfect conditions through the blood being constantly purified, that is, the elimination of poisons from the blood at regular intervals, sickness would be cut down to a bare minimum. Sad to say, people are walking around today incubating disease within their own bodies.

From the moment you are born, you start to poison yourself. Therefore, unless you are regularly decongested, you can see the amount of poisoning you put into your own body in the course of fifty years. Is it any wonder that people end up with sickness?

THE TECHNIQUE

The simple techniques set out in this book will help you to rearrange your thinking, will set you upon spiritual and physical paths to start now to eliminate poisons from your body. In this book I have covered as many complaints as possible. Obviously there are many others which I have not specifically mentioned. It can only do you good, it can only decongest, it can never do you any harm. It is completely harmless and safe. All you need are your fingers and your thumbs. Make certain that your nails are cut short because you don't want to lacerate your skin. Work with a short nail, obviously. Use the top joint of the thumb. Place the top of the thmb over the affected part given in your respective diagrams and press into the area, rotating in a clockwise motion or anti-clockwise motion, whichever you like as long as you remember to use a rotating movement. You can use the finger tips in the same way. So you work with the top joint of the thumb or finger, pressing it into the affected part and rotating.

You may find it is quite painful in the beginning but, over a period of time, as you eliminate poison from the particular nerve ending and stimulate the gland, the painful areas will decrease, until eventually there is no tenderness left in that particular area. When you have done that, you have done a good job!

Chapter 4

GENERAL CONDITIONS

Anaemia

For those who suffer from anaemic conditions, the liver and spleen, adrenals, pituitary and thyroid must be given close attention over a period of time to improve this condition.

Arthritis

To treat arthritis, rheumatism, neuritis, we must give attention to the pituitary gland because it is the master gland and controls the glandular system. If the pituitary malfunctions this can cause chaos with other glands. I have found in arthritis that those other glands are usually the thyroid and the adrenal glands. Be prepared to work well and most of all, have patience.

Asthma

A very distressing complaint caused by a deficiency in adrenalin secretions. Good work must be done upon the adrenal glands. They must be restored to a normal working condition. Also work must be done to the lung and bronchial areas. These areas can be found between and slightly under the 2nd and 3rd toes. Also work pituitary and thyroid glands.

Back-ache

Back-ache can be a sign of many things — muscle strain, arthritis, lumbago or slipped disc.

Treatment — all areas of the spinal column and big toes should be pressurised. Also the hip reflex must be worked. If the pain persists, seek medical advice.

Bad Circulation

Cold feet and cold hands are sure signs of bad circulation. The areas to work on are liver, pancreas, adrenal, kidney, pituitary, thyroid, prostate or ovary.

Plenty of salads and fresh fruit should be eaten. Physical exercise and breathing exercises should be done followed by relaxation and prayer.

Bronchitis

Bronchitis is a condition which affects the bronchial tubes and the membraneous tissue in the lung area, and the nervous system. Catarrh and phlegm are very evident in this distressing condition. Apart from staying indoors and keeping the body warm, I found that work over the area of the lungs, sinus, pituitary, thyroid, kidneys, pancreas, adrenals and colons brought about a marked improvement. Always seek medical advice in this condition.

Catarrh

Catarrh blocks up the air passages making breathing very difficult. It is caused by excessive secretion from mucous membranes and is a very distressing condition. It makes sleeping very difficult because the catarrh is falling into the back of the throat.

The treatment is to work on all sinus positions, all areas of the big toes and thumbs, the pituitary, thyroid, liver, gall bladder, ileo cecal and colons. These should be given attention at all times.

Colic

With Colic, spasmodic attacks are very possible. It can be caused by undigested substance, and the contraction is an attempt to move it.

Treatment — put pressure over all colon reflex points; work the liver, gall bladder, adrenals and kidneys. Work well and be patient. Drink plenty of warm water and examine your diet and modify it if necessary.

Constipation

Work on liver and colons. Drink plenty of hot water. Do not eat starchy foods such as white bread and cakes. Eat plenty of fresh fruit and green vegetables, also salads. Give yourself exercise if possible for stomach muscles. Show determination and patience.

Coughs

Where coughing is persistent medical advice must be sought because it could lead to Bronchitis and the lungs could become infected.

The treatment is all lung areas and chest to be worked and also all sinus areas, big toes, pituitary, thyroid, adrenals and kidneys. Have patience. Be determined.

Cystitis

For this distressing condition work upon the kidneys, bladder, adrenals, prostate or ovary. Work gently. Have determination and patience until all congestion is dispersed from the affected areas.

Dandruff

Dandruff is mostly caused by pollution in the atmosphere, combined with sweat from the scalp which creates a scaling which fastens itself to the scalp.

Treatment: Wash hair regularly. Use a good stiff brush daily on the scalp, to loosen and remove all dust and scaling. Wash head two or three times a week. Dry thoroughly then rub glycerine and olive oil into the scalp — an equal amount of each. This will help you greatly to conquer dandruff.

Diabetes

Diabetes is usually caused by shock or grief. These affect the glandular system and create a situation where insufficient insulin is being produced by the pancreas.

If the patients are already taking Insulin then they should pay heed to the fact that when the pancreas starts to supply insulin into the blood stream, in addition to the insulin they are taking, procedure must be followed as for insulin shock for which their own psysician would recommend an immediate intake of extra sugar.

Treatment is pancreas, pituitary, thyroids, adrenals and all eye and kidney areas. Work gently and well; have faith in what you do.

Digestive troubles

For digestive troubles and a bad taste in the mouth. Treatment is massage over liver, kidneys, pancreas, ascending and descending colons and central nervous systems.

Dizziness

Give pressure all over big toes and thumbs, particularly the pituitary gland and also eyes, ears and sinus areas. Make sure the liver is functioning properly. Adrenals and kidneys should also be given attention.

Ears

Much can be done to assist the ears to function properly. Give pressure to the first joint of the ring finger and little finger and to the fourth and little toes. Make sure the liver, pituitary and adrenal glands are free from congestion.

Eyes

Give pressure to the entire top joint and into the joint of first and second fingers on both hands; also first and second toes on each foot. Have your teeth checked to ascertain that they are in good order. Teeth can and do affect the eyes. Give the kidneys and adrenals treatment. At all times show faith, determination and patience.

Fertility

Many young married people come to see me because they fail to have children. This problem, more often than not, is because the hormone supply to the reproductive organs is in an unbalanced state. Normally it is the wives whom I see first but let me hasten to point out that very often it is the husband who is at fault but the male ego being what it is, nearly always believes that it cannot be him.

Eventually I end up treating both of them.

To the men I would say this — be kind, gentle and understanding and help in every way; do not give your wife a nervous complex over this problem. Marriage must be on a spiritual basis. Put your heart and soul into it. Love, honesty, sincerity, kindness and integrity are the foundation stones.

The treatment is pituitary gland, thyroid, pancreas, adrenals and ovaries for the female, prostate for the male. Whenever possible do physical exercises providing you are young and fit, followed by relaxation and prayer.

Haemorrhoids

Haemorrhoids and rectum disorders are often painful and uncomfortable. This is mostly caused by varicose veins in the rectum causing great irritation and distress. However you can take much comfort from the fact that this treatment applied properly will do wonders for these disorders and in most cases will completely clear the entire trouble out of the area.

Apply gentle pressure over the area marked on the figure drawing every forty-eight hours and work gently for a period of weeks until all tenderness disappears.

Remember most conditions will respond to Zonal Treatment. Try and use your commonsense and don't ever overdo any work on any area. Work slowly and work well.

Hay Fever

Give pressure to all colons, to the sinus areas, pituitary, adrenals and kidney glands. Be gentle, especially over the kidneys. Always have faith in what you do. Be determined and have patience. Remember Rome was not built in a day.

Headache

Headache can be caused by sinus, cervicals, indigestion, teeth and worry. Also constipation may be the cause.

Treatment — all areas of the big toes and thumbs must be worked; also all sinus, eyes, ears, cervicals, pituitary, thyroid, liver, adrenal, kidney and colon areas must be given good attention.

Heart

Gently give pressure over thumbs and fingers and pads where the fingers join the hands; all toes and pads where the toes join the feet; and the heart reflex as shown on charts.

Make certain the pituitary, thyroid, liver, kidneys, pancreas and adrenals are decongested. Have determination and be very patient.

High Blood Pressure

Hypertension can be considered a very important factor in the cause of high blood pressure. One thing is certain. There is definitely a deficiency and irregularity in the functioning of the glandular system. It is the duty of the glands to supply the body with the correct amount of hormones and adrenalin to normalise the circulation which is of vital importance in maintaining proper chemical balance.

Therefore if elimination from the system of the body is faulty, we get congestion somewhere. For instance, if we have an abnormal amount of calcium, this will stick to the walls of the arteries so that they no longer retain their normal elasticity. This increases the effort put upon the heart in performing its duty.

If a person is in a highly nervous state or suffering from what we call Hypertension, it automatically creates unbalance in the digestion. By removing the tension and reorganising the balance of the glandular system, we can bring about a wonderful change in this condition.

Blood pressure is often a problem during the latter years. It results when the walls of the blood vessels become smaller. As the walls become smaller the pressure becomes greater. The danger of tremendous pressure against the walls of the blood vessels is that it may cause a blood vessel to break. When this happens a clot is formed which may lodge in the small capillaries of the brain which causes paralysis or it could happen in the heart muscle causing angina. Such a clot can shut off the flow of blood to the heart to such an extent as to be fatal.

If a person gets into a highly nervous state this can

cause the tissues in the wall of the blood vessels to contract. During strong emotions the body normally prepares itself for action necessary to overcome this difficulty, and the walls of the blood vessels normally contract in order that the rate of pressure may be exerted against them. Such blood pressure can be made normal only when the person's nervousness or irritability or mental state which is causing the emotion is removed. Therefore anyone suffering with blood pressure should always try to remain calm and relaxed at all times because sudden activity of any part of the body increases the blood pressure in that part of the body.

If you carefully observe these rules it will help you to gain control over your condition. You can see now how vital it is to keep all the circulation of the body in perfect condition. You can see how vital it is that all glandular systems should be kept in perfect condition. This is your body. It is the only one you possess. Therefore it is up to you to take particularly good care of it.

Work with care upon the pituitary, the thyroid, all areas of the big toes and thumbs, the liver, pancreas, adrenals and kidneys and central nervous system.

Insomnia

If you suffer from insomnia, you have my deepest sympathy. To be awake all night with the imagination running riot is no joke, especially when you have to go to work after a sleepless night. I have found that good work upon the pituitary and thyroid glands brought about excellent results. Also correct any malfunction in the pancreas, adrenals and the kidneys.

This distressing complaint is usually caused through hypertension which can be any form of worry or anxiety or emotional involvement. These affect the nervous system which in turn will create havoc within the glandular system.

Lumbago

The muscles of the back are usually affected by Lumbago. This can be caused by getting cold in the kidney areas of the back or by not having sufficient clothing to protect the back. It can also be caused by excessive exercise or by lifting heavy weights. The muscles become inflamed and the nerves become pressurized.

The treatment is all spinal reflexes, the hip and back areas, also the big toes, kidneys, Pressure must be gentle. Have patience at all times.

Menopause

The treatment for Menopause is the entire glandular system — pituitary, thyroids, adrenals, liver, gall bladder, kidneys, pancreas and ovary areas. Try to work all congestion out. This will help to bring about a marked improvement over the entire glandular and nervous systems. Work well, be confident. Above all be patient.

Migraine

For migraine make sure that the pituitary, liver and gall bladder are in good order. Work all areas appertaining to eyes and ears, also all sinus areas must be pressurized. Also look for any other tender spots on the feet. Work on both thumbs and all top joints of the fingers.

Nerve Force

A simple exercise for stimulating nerve force through-out the body is to rub the finger nails together. Not only will this invigorate your nervous system but it will do wonders for falling hair and if persisted with it un-doubtedly makes the hair thick and beautiful. Don't expect a miracle overnight, you won't obtain it. What you must do is to be dedicated and determined. Do the exercise for a period of ten minutes daily — and that means everyday — if you want success.

Nervous Disorders

Agoraphobia, claustrophobia, anxiety neurosis, nervous debility, nervous asthma, strain and stress and general fears are, in the main caused by an unbalanced glandular system, which in turn unbalances the nervous systems, as one system counteracts the other. It is estimated that millions suffer from these disorders.

I have treated large numbers of patients who fall into these categories. Those I have given treatment to successfully include those completely unable to travel by any form of public transport, unable to do their own shopping, unable to go out to social occasions. The very thought of doing any of the above resulted in contraction of the stomach and solar plexus ,tightening in the chest and throat, weakness in the legs and the knees. Patients I have known have been rooted to the spot with fear; some so bad they were quite incapable of going to the door to pay the milkman.

The results that follow, once confidence is retrieved, are amazing.

If you, therefore, suffer from this kind of condition, if you suffer from any of these phobias, do not believe all is lost. What you can believe is that you are following the wrong formula. In God's world, in God's eyes, in God's knowledge, there is a cure for all who seek the right formula. Belief and faith in God, absolute faith, are the essentials.

I ask you sincerely never to give up hope. If you have the tenacity to stick it ,the results are wonderful and extremely gratifying. Let us examine the form of treatment. First of all we re-establish a beautifully balanced glandular system and a beautiful, vigorous, purified bloodstream. This is then followed by physical exercises, breathing exercises and meditation.

To help all who suffer from these forms of nervous disorders I have made an LP recording which describes in detail how to generate and stimulate the nervous systems and how to use the Holy Breath, which is Life Force, to stimulate the different nervous systems of the body. It also explains and gives a most beautiful meditation which, if practised, will induce calmness, tranquillity and spiritual enlightenment. The musical background for the recording is absolutely superb. It is the wonderful sound of a 32-piece orchestra playing the most beautiful music. This record should be in the possession of everyone whether healthy or sick, for it is a recording that shows the way and opens up the path to true spiritual enlightenment through the subconscious mind, the gateway to the Infinite Intelligence. I also highly recommend it for all forms of asthma, sinus and catarrhal conditions, purely for the breathing techniques given on it.

In my experience I have found that the offending glands in nervous conditions are usually the pituitary gland, thyroid and parathyroid, and the central nervous system.

Numbness

The circulation must be attended to, the pituitary, liver, kidneys, thyroid, adrenals and pancreas. Also use a wire brush or a comb and stroke upwards over back of hands and up the arms. This helps the circulation. Be persistent and patient.

Poor Vitality

Work upon the adrenal glands in particular then pay attention to the pituitary and thyroid. Be sure you are eating enough protein. You cannot have energy if you are not putting the energy into your body. Work well and be patient.

Prostate trouble

Around the age of 45 to 65 trouble with the prostate gland is always a possibility. The glands to work are pituitary, prostate, bladder, kidney, pancreas, liver, adrenal, ascending and descending colons; also the sacro iliac and coccyx areas.

Physical exercise should be taken, also breathing exercises, relaxation and prayer. Be determined. Show patience. Be gentle.

Sciatica

Sciatica is caused by inflammation of the sciatic nerve which runs down the back of the thigh. The condition can be brought on by various things — pressure on any nerve in the spine, a slipped disc or extreme dampness.

Treatment — work all areas of the big toes including cervicals and spinal column. Pay close attention to the hip reflex, bladder and the kidneys.

Sinus

Inflammation or infection can spread into the sinus cavities. When this happens the condition becomes painful and breathing becomes difficult.

Treatment — all sinus areas, chest and lungs, throat, ears, eyes, liver, kidney and ileo cecal and colons must be decongested. Also drink plenty of hot water.

The Spine—Backbone

It must be remembered that the spine or backbone is composed of a number of pieces of bone called vertebrae, joined by connective tissue.

This part of the body should be regularly stretched. Think about walking tall. Think tall. Be as tall as a mountain stretched towards the clouds. Remember that unless that part of your body is kept at full stretch it will contract, and if this state of affairs is allowed to go on unchecked for a long period of time, you will become permanently shrunk or shortened. Don't slouch or allow your shoulders to droop. Pull yourself up with a jerk; straighten your back; be mentally alert; physically adjust your posture.

THINK TALL until it becomes second nature. It is of vital importance. You are what you think you are.

Spondylitis

Severe neck trouble, particularly seated in the cervical region, a very painful complaint.

The treatment is all areas of the spinal column and the big toes and thumbs must be worked very gently and with a lot of patience.

Stomach trouble

Treatment — Thumbs and top joints of fingers must be worked; also give pressure over the entire back of the hands. Give liver, pancreas, adrenals, kidneys, ileo cecal and colons attention to remove congestion. Drink plenty of hot water.

Teeth and Tooth or Gum Ache

Treatment — Give pressure over all finger top joints and on all the pads where the fingers join the hand, also on thumbs. Give pressure on all toes and pads where the toes join the feet. Work for a few minutes, give it a rest and then restart. Make the entire operation about 20 minutes. Seek dental treatment as soon as possible.

Throat trouble

Treatment: all areas of throat and all sinus positions including main sinus, eye sinus, ear sinus; also lungs and chest. Work well and have patience.

Tongue

Pay attention to your tongue. It plays a vital role in your health. Acidity and poison coat the tongue and this should be removed daily.

Treatment: each morning and evening when cleaning your teeth, take a dry towel and pull your tongue out and clean it with a toothbrush. This is of paramount importance to your health and also helps to eliminate bad breath.

Varicose Veins

In my experience I found that the kidney, liver, pancreas and colons usually showed signs of deep congestion. Be determined and work gently until all congestion is dispersed.

Vertigo

Vertigo, dizziness or a feeling of giddiness comes mainly from the internal ear or eyes or sometimes from stomach disorder, headache or poor circulation. Treatment — give pressure over ear and eye reflex, all sinus, the big toes and thumbs and all top joints of fingers. Also the pituitary, thyroid, liver and kidneys. If persistent seek medical advice.

Prevention

Don't forget that for any kind of throat trouble you must pull out your tongue, take hold of it with a dry piece of cloth or towel and pull your tongue gently and move it about. This stimulates the 60 odd muscles in your throat.

You have depressor muscles and elevator muscles in your throat, about sixty, which need constant stimulation.

If you work upon these lines many, many things that you have will disappear.

You will find that the treatment is good for complaints like Haemorrhoids, uterine troubles and constipation. So many little troubles that can be purgatory if you don't know how to relieve them. So get rid of them by doing this kind of treatment. It is the nearest you can get to total prevention. Prevention is better than cure. Far better to prevent a thing than to have it. Make sure that you never get it.

This is the whole concept of zonal treatment. It is to prevent you from getting things.

What I want you to remember at all times is this. Where there is any painful area it means there is congestion and it should be worked out.

Stimulation

You will find that pressure over the fingers and the toes alone will help to prevent many things. It helps to build up your nerve force if you are suffering with nervousness or other complaints.

Daily work over all the fingers and all the toes will help to stimulate the nervous systems and builds up the nerve strength in the body. It will help you to relieve all these symptoms. It will also help you with nausea or any form of sickness, sea-sickness or air sickness. This kind of treatment will help to relieve and abate all sickness. It is good for neuralgia or neuritis or cramps. It helps to stimulate the circulation so that if you do suffer from cold feet or cold hands you will find that regular practice on these lines will greatly help to rectify conditions of all kinds. You can take a nice mild wire brush and stroke up your legs, over your feet, your hands, up your arms, stroke upwards not downwards. This all helps to stimulate the circulation.

All kinds of complaints will respond to this form of treatment — stomach aches, tired feelings, ulcerated stomachs, throat troubles, laryngitis, loss of voice will all respond to zonal treatments. There are not many things that will not respond. Indigestion will respond, even pain in your mouth from teeth or gums will respond to this treatment.

Ignorance

I have tried to make the information in this book as plain and as simple as possible so that anyone can understand it. Most of the diseases and complaints that the average person develops are through ignorance. Ignorance of the fact that there is a very simple way in which you can keep the mechanics of your body in perfect order. Like taking the car in for a regular service. Some people take their cars in for regular service and therefore have trouble-free motoring. Other people never take their cars to be serviced with the result that they wear out and the car will come to a stop, apart from all the trouble it gives them in between. This is exactly the same with human bodies. You keep eating and drinking until eventually you poison yourself. Now if you had a regular method of decongesting yourself, of giving yourself a regular service, most of these things would never happen to you. Remember from the little acorn grows the big oak tree and from a little bit of congestion eventually grows a big disease. Get that fact firmly into your head and never forget it!

Right Sole

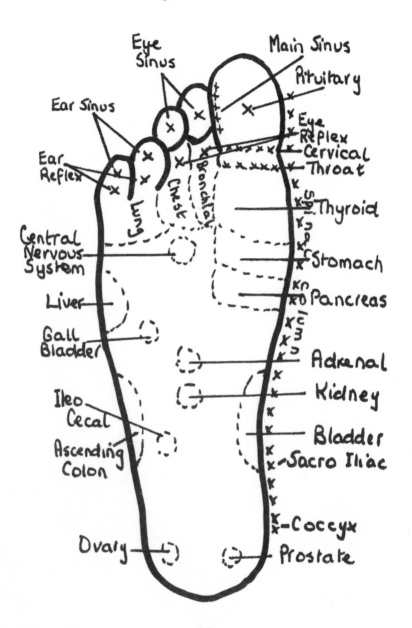

Eye Sinus

Main Sinus

Pituitary

Ear Sinus

Eye Reflex

Ear Reflex

Cervical

Throat

Lung

Chest

Bronchial

Thyroid

Central Nervous System

Stomach

Liver

Pancreas

Gall Bladder

Adrenal

Kidney

Ileo Cecal

Bladder

Ascending Colon

Sacro Iliac

Coccyx

Ovary

Prostate

Left Sole

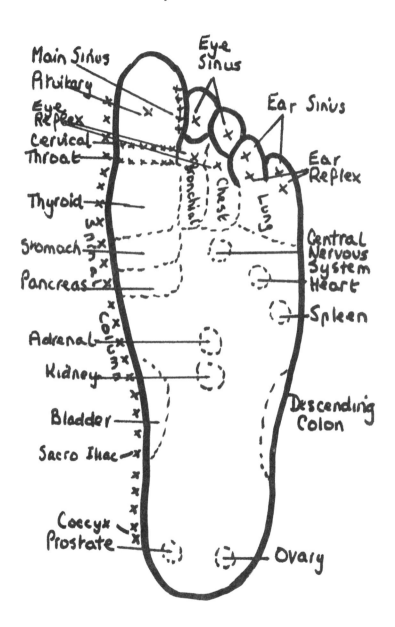

87

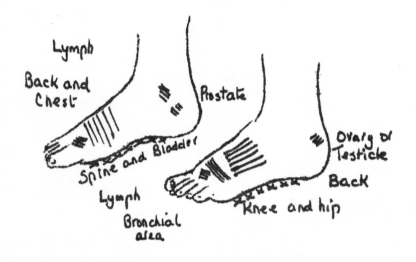

Lymph

Back and Chest

Prostate

Ovary or Testicle

Spine and Bladder

Back

Lymph

Knee and hip

Bronchial area

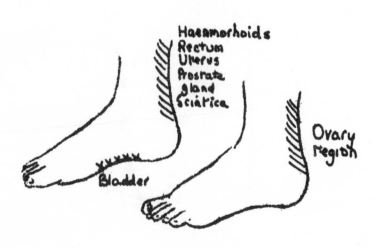

Haemorhoids
Rectum
Uterus
Prostate gland
Sciatica

Ovary region

Bladder

Chapter 5

THE BODY BEAUTIFUL

If you want a beautiful healthy body you must make certain that you get plenty of sleep and relaxation. Your muscles need time to recuperate and to build up. If you are working during the day on any job, particularly if you are doing a physical job, then you must remember that your muscle cells are being broken down by the repeated tension. These cells must be given rest periods to enable them to re-build and to increase their overall muscle size. So you must take periods of physical relaxation when you can.

You must also try to conserve your energy. Rest at all opportunities especially after meals and try to make certain that you always have at least eight hours sleep every night.

NUTRITION

Always try to eat well. Don't starve yourself. Nutrition is tremendously important. Remember you are what you eat. Don't fill up on what we call "foodless foods", like white flour products, chocolates and candies and all of the other products which have no benefits at all. Try and eat a balanced diet of vegetables and salads. Fish, eggs, a little meat (not a pound a day) as you need the protein. Remember you are mostly protein and this is what you need, protein, and fruit and milk. If you find that you are too fat then in the first place you should reduce on potatoes, bread, sugar, pastry and drink skimmed milk. And if you are on the thin side, then you must remember that your muscles cannot enlarge unless you are taking in enough protein to enable this enlargement to take place. So eat more if you are on the thin side. Still remembering not to eat "foodless foods".

The best way to eat is to have four or five small meals per day, because this prevents your stomach from being over-stretched which happens when you eat one big meal and which gives you a terrible bloated feeling. And, apart from that, eating four or five small meals per day gives your body a more constant food supply and you will find that the muscles of your body are being fed more regularly.

Everyone should attempt always to have a good breakfast before going out to work as this sets the pattern for the day. It feeds the body immediately and helps you to get a good start. If you go to work on an empty stomach then you are tired before you begin.

CONCENTRATION

Put your mind to what you are doing. This will improve your performance greatly. The concentration inspires you to improve your work on your body. It is very difficult to give your mind to anything completely so you must try to work up enthusiasm about what you are doing.

Take a good look at yourself in the mirror. Strip off your clothes, have a good look at yourself and then think of how you would like to look. Think of the kind of body you would love to have, and from that moment on, work towards obtaining that kind of body.

INSPIRATION

This is the greatest inspiration you can give yourself. Be positive. Don't be negative in your attitudes. Think to yourself — I am going to be better, I am going to improve myself 100 per cent. Imagine yourself beautifully muscular, keep a mental image of what you are striving to construct. Say to yourself — I will succeed.

Be determined that you will keep up your enthusiasm until success is yours.

BE CARING

Remember that once your glandular systems and your nervous systems are working perfectly you then have to build up and take care of your body. Exercise, physical, exercise, is essential unless you are severely handicapped.

Other things which have to be taken care of are your skin, your teeth and your hair.

Besides feeding your skin from the inside you must also care for it from the outside because your skin is directly exposed to the physical environment you are living in. It has to cope with changes of temperature, too much sunshine or too little sunshine, wind, fumes, fog, soot, smoke and dust, and also the central heating conditions most of us are living in.

Due to all these things your skin is constantly losing natural oils. Your skin has to be oiled to help it to conserve its own moisture so that it remains smooth and supple. The natural oils give you your beautiful skin.

DO NOT WORRY

Anxiety and worry do start skin troubles. Worry and emotional upsets can harm your blood vessels which also in turn cause skin complications. And besides worry does create lines in your skin which age you very quickly. So if you want to keep a good young face, then relaxation is what you must practise. Stop all the frowning and furrowing that goes with a worried face. Practise relaxation for your skin.

SKIN CARE

If you do have blackheads or open pores a good thing to do is to take some form of cooking utensil or bowl and fill it with very hot water and then place the bowl on the table, cover your head with a big bath towel so that all the steam is under the towel and steam your face. Make certain that the steam is not escaping to get the best benefit. You want the steam to rise straight up into your face. You could put any form of small herbs into the hot water. You will find that the steam will penetrate deeply into your pores and perspiration will pour down from the open pores which loosens the accumulated dirt and rancid oils. After that close the pores with cold water, as cold as possible.

Do this on three consecutive days for no more than five or ten minutes at a time.

After that, if you do it once a week it would help to keep all the pores clean, giving you a lovely beautiful look.

It is very difficult if you are a city dweller to partake in fresh air exercises such as taking good walks. Your skin, believe it or not, does need exposure to clean fresh air, a good walk over fields or woodlands. Air bathing you could call it. And it has enormous benefits to give.

SLEEP

Always make certain if you want to keep a beautiful youthful face, that is a beautiful skin, that you have sufficient sleep. Insufficient sleep will make you look old quicker than anything and you will have bags under the eyes, crow's feet, etc. So try to make certain that you do form habits of going to bed early. Otherwise, if you neglect your sleep the skin will become lifeless, will lose its elasticity and become exceedingly dull.

SMOKING

Smoking is another quick way to ruin the skin. You see heavy smokers whose skin looks parched and is a yellowish colour. Nicotine plays havoc with the skin. Think of the amount of poison in tobacco smoke which you inhale and which passes down into your body through your bloodstream.

If you are putting poison into your blood, how do you expect to look beautiful? If you are a heavy smoker it is impossible to have a truly healthy glowing skin.

CONSTIPATION

Another thing that makes the skin dull and unclear is constipation. A lot of people take laxatives hoping that it will solve the problem. What will solve the problem is if you are eating the correct foods and taking the correct exercise, and also having the correct amount of rest, sleep and relaxation. If you suffer from constipation you must eat plenty of fresh fruit and vegetables.

HAIR CARE

How about your hair? If you are losing your hair and going thin on top, it's very worrying isn't it. But there are things that can be done to help these conditions. Remember the exercise of rubbing your finger nails together to stimulate all the nerve endings up to the hair roots. You should buffer your fingernails together for 15 minutes per day. You don't have to do the 15 minutes all at once — a few minutes at a time to make up 15 minutes in a day.

HYGIENE

Now it is very important that we take care of the hair in other ways. So hygiene is also very important. If you live in a city your hair will need much more care than if you live in the country because of the amount of dirt which blocks up the hair follicles and causes premature baldness. If you want thick hair all your life then your head should be the cleanest part of your body. You must therefore pay particular attention to keeping it clean. You must see that it gets plenty of air and sunshine. Never wear a tight hat because this blocks off all air supply and induces sweat which corrodes the hair.

SUN TREATMENT

The sun is vital for good hair because it encourages growth through the energy it gives to the hair. The rays of the sun strengthen your hair and help it in its growth so subject your hair to the sun whenever you can. Try to get the sun to reach the roots of your hair as much as possible. Walk out in the wind, let the wind flow through your hair. This is immensely invigorating, stimulating and exhilarating.

Be careful what you use in the form of hair sprays and lacquers because they settle, crystallise and eat into the pores clogging them up and so ruin your hair. Be very careful what you use.

MASSAGE

Use plenty of finger massage on the hair. Apply the fingers to the scalp and then, without lifting them, massage deep into your scalp from the back to the front until you have covered the entire head. Try to make a daily habit of giving your scalp a massage. The action induces a free flow of blood to the roots of the hair and is one more positive step towards making sure that you are doing the best you can towards keeping a beautiful head of hair.

PROTEIN

Again your hair is made of protein so you must make certain that you are getting adequate supplies of good protein. As I have said before, fish, nuts, cheese, milk, poultry, not too much meat, soya beans, eggs will provide the protein which is essential for good health.

NATURAL WAYS

Assist nature in every way and don't fool yourself because if there were any lotions that could make hair grow on bald heads, we wouldn't have any bald people around. Think of all the famous people who have expensive hair transplants. They surely wouldn't do this if they could rub some lotion into their scalp and the hair would grow. No, natural ways are the only ways open to you — to keep your hair clean and well brushed.

CLEANLINESS

Brush your hair regularly taking all the dead hair out of your head, the roots that die there and stay there if you don't brush your hair regularly will clog up all the pores. Keep your combs and brushes scrupulously clean. Cleanliness is the guide.

Also, once a week you should make a habit of gently pulling your hair, grabbing hold of the tufts of hair all over the head and gently pulling. As your hair strengthens you can increase the exercise by adding more strength to the tugging movement.

CORRECT POSTURE

The majority of people hold their bodies incorrectly during their waking hours. People allow the abdomen to swell out. This is mostly due to incorrect breathing. As a result the abdomen enlarges and this causes a sagging of the colons, internal organs, intestines and displacements so that you have a corporation, a swollen stomach. This incorrect breathing and the sagging of the abdomen muscles pulls forward on the lumbar and the dorsal areas of the spine. If this is allowed to go on, apart from walking around with a large stomach all the time, the arches begin to fall, you lose control over all the back muscles and the muscles in the stomach begin to dissipate.

So you must learn to walk and to sit straight. Walk erectly. Breathe deeply and steadily and you must consciously hold the abdomen up by the internal muscles. You must walk with shoulders back, head erect and abdomen up and in. You should breathe deeply, pull your abdomen in and lift your chest up. You must practise this to regain control over your abdominal muscles. Make a habit of walking correctly with your stomach in and your chest out. In the beginning you will find discomfort because the muscles will not want to work but you must persist to regain correct posture. And the reward is well worth the trouble. You will find that your fallen arches will straighten up and your height will increase. In addition your bowel action and your digestion and your general health will benefit as a result of seeing that you do walk correctly and that your posture is how it should be.

TEETH AND MOUTH

Always see your dentist regularly. Make sure that your teeth are in first class condition. Do not allow your teeth to go bad because it poisons the bloodstream. Bad teeth can be the cause of many diseases. If you have bad teeth then that indirectly helps to poison your scalp, apart from all the many other diseases that can accrue from having bad teeth. So you should make certain that you keep your teeth spotlessly clean and your mouth spotlessly clean. Try if possible always to clean your mouth and your teeth after each and every meal.

Be determined to try to do everything to get your body into perfect shape starting with your glands and your nervous systems and then working outwards to your skin care, to your teeth and mouth care and your hair care.

This is your body. Again I repeat it is the only one you are ever likely to have whilst you are here. You must take the most dedicated care of it.

MAIN DENOMINATOR

Over the many years that I have been healing and treating patients I have met practically every complaint there is. I find that there is one main denominator to success and that is to be able to inspire the patient to take a natural interest in their own body, a desire to succeed, a desire to become 100 per cent. fit. Once this state of mind is acquired it usually ends in success.

HOW TO LOSE WEIGHT

The most common question I get is "How can I lose weight and become slim and youthful looking?" The person who usually asks this question is of course someone who is flabby around the waist and the hips and wishes to regain youthful slenderness. Others are just simply fat and want to lose weight.

The answer is very simple. Although one can hardly these days glance through a magazine or a newspaper without finding some super-duper, sure-fire way of reducing weight through dieting, yet the real facts are very uncomplicated.

Remember this, there are no fantastic secrets about the business of losing weight. So I am going to tell you a system I have practised for years.

Losing weight is a matter of gradually reducing calories. This is easily done by cutting out foods with a high calory content whilst, at the same time, making sure the body gets enough vitamins, minerals and proteins to stay healthy. First of all, always check with your doctor to make certain that you are in a healthy condition to proceed with any diet or loss of weight. After which it becomes simple. Systematically reduce all sugar, potatoes, bananas, pastas, white bread, fried foods, cookies, cakes and sweets. Eat tomatoes, fish, lean meat, eggs, cheese, celery and all types of fruit and vegetables (except bananas), drink skimmed milk.

Don't forget that, once you start to do this, exercise is of great importance because it helps to draw up and firm the loose skin left over after substantial weight loss takes place. It will also help you to build up energy which dieting alone does not give.

A good idea is to take a multi vitamin-mineral pill each day and I suggest that you take a protein supplement to ensure that your body is getting all the goodness it requires.

A most important thing to remember in losing weight is to reduce your food and liquid intake a little more each day. If you persist in this your weight will go down.

Then once you have reached the desired weight you want, adjust your eating habits so that you maintain that weight for the rest of your life. Always be conscious of the fact that if you go back to the kind of eating habits you had previously before you decided to lose weight, you will very quickly return to your old flabby body again.

No secrets about it. Discipline is what you need and common sense.

RELAXATION

When the mind and body are persistently overworked through the stress and strain of our so-called civilised world which includes food, drink, social activities and all the other forms of entertainment available, their natural function rapidly decreases. It is a very difficult thing for modern man to learn the art of proper relaxation as he has obviously forgotten that nature required the body and mind to relax to enable nature to recharge them.

Today, even if you are taking so-called "rest", you

are either watching television or reading or are engaged in some form of mental or muscular tension. Therefore you are constantly expending vital energy. There isn't much use in increasing your output if you are going to waste it unnecessarily.

Therefore you should lie down, stretch a few times and then completely relax by mentally going over the body. Start with your feet and work up through the legs, through the body into the head, shoulders, arms and spine. Even your mouth and throat and tongue and eyes should be completely relaxed. Every part of you should be completely relaxed. Breathing in a nice easy way you should mentally relax every part of the body.

Everything you do in this life requires a fantastic amount of energy. Therefore you are always tensed up and some people spend their entire lives in a constantly tensed up state. Remember that every action, conscious or unconscious, uses up vital force. This is the electro magnetic force which is constantly running through your body. In the conscious state the conscious mind sends a message to the sub-conscious mind, which immediately obeys by sending the force to the desired part.

Imagine then the amount of power one uses up in a normal working day and you can see the absolute necessity to relax and to consciously relax, to know that you are relaxing and to work at relaxing.

Every muscular movement or any emotion like worry, anxiety, anger, rage, greed uses up the electrical force within your body and, as the force is depleted, terrific strain is put upon the physical working parts of your body, causing wholesale deterioration within the entire body structure, the glandular systems and the nervous systems. If you become annoyed or very angry, you will have noticed how weak you feel after the rage or anger has subsided. And in actual fact you are more tired at that moment than you would have been had you done a hard day's physical labour because during your anger all your muscles are tensed up, your breathing becomes irregular, your eyes become wild and all parts of your body are in a tensed up state. At that particular time, your heart is beating faster, your blood pressure is increased and all this causes devastation to the digestive systems. Imagine the shock that all this has given to the body as a whole. The devastation that is actually taking place in the nervous system is terrific.

And think how much energy is necessary to restore that force back to all the muscles, the glandular systems and the nervous systems that have taken part during that period of rage and anger. No amount of vitamins or drugs or anything else will provide an ultimate solution to anyone suffering from worries and anxieties.

Conscious relaxation is definitely the answer, and the ability to know that you are relaxing and to be in control whilst you are relaxing; and to work at relaxing. Think of the mental fatigue that takes place during a fit of anger or rage and be determined that from this moment on you are going to learn to relax properly. Learn to economise on the amount of energy you use. Consciously pace yourself so that at no time are you running your body full out, unless it is absolutely necessary. Remember that each day your body builds up the energy which is necessary for the next day and all that energy can be consumed within a few minutes by bad moods, irritation and anger, because they cause intensity within the physical body and the mind.

If you learn to relax properly you will undoubtedly build up endurance and strength. You will become vigorous and full of vitality. Take a good look at a cat. Notice how it lies down and stretches and relaxes. Notice its beautiful motion when it walks. Another thing with a cat, you will notice he will only use the necessary amount of energy required in any situation. Most of his time he spends in a relaxed condition but when he needs all his reflexes and energies, he can put them together in a split second and all that latent energy that has been lying there comes into use as he catapults forward. A cat is able to do this because he instinctively knows the power of relaxing. The power of relaxation gives him the ability to put this tremendous physical reflex into operation when required. You can learn a lot from watching a cat.

So when you are lying down relaxing, firstly allow thought forms to appear and suggest to each part of your body like your fingers, wrist, elbows, shoulders, feet, ankles, calfs or knees or thighs and the rest of your body that it should relax. Send thought forms saying, ankle, I want you to relax, wrist, I want you to relax. Suggest to each set of muscles that they completely relax; your fingers, your toes, your neck, your spine. Send the thought to each one. Tell it to completely relax. This is known as auto suggestion. You are telling and suggesting to your muscles and your internal organs that they should relax and they will do this if you ask them to do so in a relaxed way. Also think about your heart, your liver, kidneys, lungs and your brain. They need to be able to relax and if you tell them to relax, they will do so.

And now to relax yourself mentally. You do this by concentrating purely on the breath. You breathe in and consciously send the breath to every part of your body. Breathe in slowly and just completely concentrate on breathing, concentrate completely on breathing. It will give you a feeling of being as light as a feather and it will bring about a beautiful feeling of blissfulness, peace and joy.

The other part of your relaxation is spiritual relaxation and unless you induce spiritual relaxation, it is very difficult to completely remove all the other worries

102

and tensions from the mind. You must have something else you can identify yourself with. As long as you are concentrating purely on the body and the mind, you will always have worries. So you have to withdraw yourself from your body and separate yourself from your ego. To do this we think on spiritual levels. We think of Godly forces. We think in Godly ways. We offer up little prayers for guidance and blessings. Think of the Godly forces as being eternal, infinite, all powerful, all peaceful, all knowing and all loving.

Without the spiritual side of relaxation you are left purely with the evil emotions of the mind and the body which man is prey to. The only sure way of rescuing yourself from the mind and the body is by identification with the pure consciousness or soul, in other words, with the Godly and spiritual forces.

Chapter 6

THE REAL YOU

The human body is a robot with a computer which we call the Brain. All information enters the brain through the central nervous system which is often called the second brain. Now as we all know a computer must have a controller or a programmer. Who then is the controller in the human system? I suggest to you the controller must be that part of you which we could call the Observer, religiously called the Spirit or Soul. Always remember that we are invisible to each other, for all we see of a person is the outer integument, and the nearest we can get to really seeing each other is through the eyes.

The eyes are a miracle of construction, look deep into the eyes of someone who loves you and whom you also love, for it is there you see the real love pouring out. The eyes never cheat. What you really feel will always manifest through the eyes. When you are happy, successful and joyous and doing what you really love doing, there is an abundance of life and love lighting up your face, mainly through your eyes.

To be happy you must be very unselfish. The greatest happiness comes from giving. Spread your bread upon the waters and it will return a thousandfold. Always be prepared to give of your very best and always give much more than you expect in return. Let love motivate you until you radiate an abundance of love. This has the effect of making you magnetic for people love the peace and tranquillity of your presence.

You are much more than a lump of flesh and bone. You are a thought form of the divine Creator. You are the greatest miracle of all time and you must begin to believe it and to see it as the real unadulterated truth.

The vast majority of people never live, they simply exist. They could be called the living dead. It is so sad. There are millions who don't even know which side of the body the liver is on and yet it is part of them. The theme of this book is—Make your physical body perfect; get to know every part of it, ensure it is up to perfection. Then and only then can you begin to investigate the Thinking Body. So we deal firstly with the physical body. Then next comes the Thinking Body which incorporates the conscious mind and the subconscious mind, and from there we can go on to Divine Infinite Intelligence and the big one which is Universal Law.

Look at the divine gifts you possess. So you must wake up and get the best out of your life. You don't have to become a monk or a fanatic. You can live, laugh and love and be very happy making other people happy.

The Thinking Body is a very high gift for it gives you the capacity to become conscious of the Divine Law; to understand it, to work in harmony with it in all its manifestations.

When God created you it was with the idea of you becoming a co-Creator. That plan sadly misfired but if you examine it you can see what you are missing. There surely cannot be any greater or higher value in the Universe. What a force! You could be powerful in thought and having the greatest treasures possessed by man. A man should be noble and man should have the ability and freedom to accomplish whatever he truly wants. This comes about through being in harmony with the Great Law and thereby living in perfection with the eternal law.

If a man is in harmony with the divine law, he is able to cure all diseases in the physical body. He can create harmony in the Thinking Body; the Feeling Body and the Acting Body. Through all this environment can be changed and complete harmony in the world is a distinct possibility.

The Feeling Body has a natural function to express love, and the more love expressed, the nearer you become to the cosmic ocean of divine love. For divine love is a great cosmic power that can be most powerfully expressed through the Feeling Body. All the currents of deep feelings and emotions affect those around us. Love feelings are curative. Hate feelings are destructive, so be loving.

My first concern is to help you to understand more about your physical body but in other books I will write about the Thinking and Feeling bodies. I do hope the little I have written will give you an insight into the most beautiful miraculous machine ever invented. I cannot emphasise too strongly the importance of the glandular system, nervous systems and physical working parts of the body and their effect upon your entire life and your attitude towards your fellow men.

In the course of a human life, the body changes and is completely replaced every seven years. Medical science tells us that our outer integument is replaced in six months and the liver just as rapidly. This applies equally to the brain cells which could not survive in a functional state without oxygen and other essentials supplied by the bloodstream.

Therefore, if a man can remember something which happened to him forty years ago, where then is his memory? In his brain? But that is replaced every seven years. So how can he remember back forty years. The answer would seem to be that it is the "Observer" in you that remembers, that part of you which is not made of flesh and bone.

If you begin to ask yourself questions like that, you will start to appreciate the living miracle you undoubtedly are.

The business end of the Brain is the Cortex. It is surrounded by something like a thousand million neurones or nerve cells which obviously receive messages and also convey messages from and to the body by electrical means. They maintain the five small minute voltages required to keep the heart functioning in the fashion of a programmed computer.

The eyes are a miracle of construction. The Retina contains around ten million light sensitive cells, each one connected to the optic nerve by a microscopic nerve fibre. Thus a complete picture at the frequency of light is conveyed to the centre of the brain showing a picture of the world outside us. The optic nerve appears to finish in empty space and opticians will confirm that we have no means of knowing how such a picture is presented to the Observer.

The Retina, of course, only receives frequencies measured in angstroms but the appreciation of colour is something which exists only within the Observer. An angstrom is a unit of frequency for expressing the wavelengths of light, ultra-violet rays, X-rays and molecular and atomic distances.

The ear receives only the effect of vibrations by air on the ear drum but music exists only in the mind of the listener. The Observer and his robot are interlinked to an extraordinary degree. Some people are able to learn to control the physiological functions of the body, such as the slowing down or speeding up of the heartbeat.

All this is the miracle of You.

When you are Healing, that is giving or taking treatment, remember it all comes through the subconscious mind. The Infinite Intelligence programmes the subconscious. Therefore if your prayers and thoughts are good and your faith is strong, those things you desire will come true. But if you think negatively, destructively, viciously, these thoughts will also come true. It is your thoughts you must look at and examine very closely for your thonghts are you, for you do become what you think.

Your vitality, strength, weakness, financial status, work, friends and social status give a perfect reflection of the ideas you have about yourself. Your subconscious mind is always working night and day. It is the body builder. It is the real you. Unfortunately we are too busy with the conscious mind. That being so you must keep your conscious mind busy with expectations of the very best. Keep all rubbish out of it. Think lovely, true, just things. Take care of your conscious mind. Be good to it. Be of good heart, knowing that habitual thinking on lovely things becomes you. Think that the healing presence is flowing through the subconscious mind, expressing harmony, health, joy and peace in abundance. It is living Intelligence and a loving companion that will never ever desert you.

The greatest power in heaven and earth is thought. You are your thoughts. God made the Universe by thought and all creations are the thought of God. Most certainly great healings are done through great thoughts, by thinking in godly ways. I do not mean being pious, sanctimonious or "holier than thou" because that is not godly.

Retire to the quietness and peace of your room and in deep silence seek the aid of Infinite Intelligence. Practise along these lines and you will eventually be able to send out healing thoughts of such tremendous power than can change the ethers of disease and death to those of health and life.

In my work I treat patients suffering from Parkinsons Disease, Cancer, Multiple Sclerosis and other terminal complaints. I am able to do this only by the grace of Infinite Intelligence, over many years of quietly entering into the silence and listening. "Let him with ears, hear." You can all do it if you want to. It takes time, patience, determination, dedication and application but the end product will give you peace and joy. For over the years you will become the result of your thought forms. Only by entering the silence and making contact with Divine Intelligence can you hear and know the real truth. Lift up your eyes and see the safety vaults of Heaven, and open your Bank account there.

Your physical body is affected by your thinking and negative thinking will over a period of time destroy your body. It is like taking a daily dose of poison. This is why you must think positively for the best. Be determined that your physical body shall be a glowing, shining example for others to look upon. Once you have achieved that then you can begin to work on the other bodies you possess. Remember you are after superb, physical, mental and spiritual health. Never lose sight of your goal. Use imagination. Be simplicity itself. Don't complicate matters. Approach it all in a happy, joyous way. Have simple faith. Be completely committed to succeed. Have a clear-cut idea in your mind. Never use such slogans as "Things are getting worse", or "I will never solve it", or "It is hopeless", or "I'm all mixed up", for that kind of thinking is negative rubbish because it is being fed into the subconscious and eventually if you carry on like it, things *will* get worse, you will never solve it, you will be all mixed up, you will become what you are thinking.

When you treat a disease, it is not only the physical body that you treat, that is only a part of it. You are treating the entire personality and the physical disease you see is a reflection of things that have gone wrong with the thinking, feeling and acting bodies. It is of little use treating the effect if you are going to ignore the cause. Therefore the cause must be removed. So many diseases can come through the mental, feeling and acting bodies.

Poverty is a debilitating disease as those who have suffered it can testify. Poverty is not just a financial disease, it devastates the mental body. The lack of money constantly circulating in your life can eventually make you very ill because the urge of your life principle is towards growth, expansion and abundancy. You are not in this life to live in dire straits or a hovel, hungry and forlorn. You should be happy, prosperous and successful. Again you see it all comes back to how you think. Through the subconscious mind is the golden road. Think prosperously. Claim as your divine right Wealth and Happiness. Do not make money a God. See it as a means of helping you along the road to true enlightenment. Money is not evil for it is only a material. The evil comes through money being used for evil purposes. Think of money as being an aid which you will use wisely and constructively and towards good.

If you begin to think and act like this your circumstances will rapidly change, your thought forms will see to that.

All through the ages men of all nations have believed that somewhere there is a vast untapped store of healing power which could restore to normal the functions of man's body and that as a result the alleviation of suffering would follow.

That there is a source of healing power is undoubtedly

true. My experience has led me to the conclusion that basically we are a special species and that as Jesus so often said: "I am in the Father and the Father is in me". I must say I absolutely agree with that definite statement. God, divine infinite Intelligence, is released into a human being through the subconscious mind. I take that as a fact of life because it is something you can get to grips with.

You can pray until you are blue in the face but if you are doing it all wrong, you will not go very far. Mankind must become aware of the subconscious mind. Prayer should be directed through that channel, then positive results will follow. Jesus insisted upon Faith. Over and over again he said, "According to your Faith it is done unto you".

For instance, if you plant seeds in the ground, you have the faith that they will grow, for that is what seeds do. Faith is a seed. If you plant that into the subconscious, it will also grow.

Faith is the acceptance by the subconscious mind of matter which the conscious mind would reject, a complete reliance on the power of the subconscious mind is needed. Matthew ch. 9, 28-30 — "And when he was come into the house, the blind men came to him: and Jesus saith unto them, Believe ye that I am able to do this? They said unto him, Yea Lord. Then he touched their eyes saying, According to your Faith be it unto you, and their eyes were opened".

This shows that their faith was the main factor — that inner conviction that something miraculous would happen with Jesus.

The same thing will happen for you in all walks of life if you have the same faith in whatsoever you do in your work or position, in your love life, if you had absolute faith that the right person for you would come along, it would happen. The kind of faith we are talking about is, of course, real faith and not the lip service kind of faith so commonly used. Real faith is where the imagination is aroused to an intense degree and the certainty that the thing will happen.

The underlying principle here is the subconscious mind and the one process of healing is Faith.

Practise the understanding of patience, kindness, love, joy, happiness, wisdom, goodwill and understanding, for they are qualities which never grow old. Cultivate these. Express them and remain young in body and spirit.

Your faith and convictions are ageless. If you make it a daily practice to love, be joyous, to laugh and to seek inner peace, you will never grow old.

So here you have it. Perfect conditioning of the physical body comes first, then the principle of correct thinking and feeling and acting. Always put into effect the work on the subconscious to the best of your ability especially just before sleep and it is then that the Infinite Intelligence will talk to you. It is where you will experience flashes of inspiration; where you will gain knowledge that you never had before. It is there and yours for the asking.

If you ask you will receive. Have no doubt. Just plug into it. You don't have to learn anything. It is already there, always has been, you simply have to recollect it. All you have to do is to be silent. The Power of the Universe is behind you. Every day can be perfect if you so desire.

Read this book and put the information into practice. Be determined not to be mediocre. Enjoy your life, it can be very beautiful for you. With God behind you, how can you go wrong.